50 Songs With Sax App

CW00552733

Wise Publications
London/New York/Paris/Sydney/Copenhagen/Madrid

Exclusive Distributors
Music Sales Limited
8-9 Frith Street,
London W1V 5TZ, England.
Music Sales Pty Limited
120 Rothschild Avenue,
Rosebery, NSW 2018,
Australia.

Order No. AM952810
ISBN 0-7119-7326-1

Designed by Pearce Marchbank, Studio Twenty.
Compiled by Jack Long.
Printed in the United Kingdom by
Redwood Books Limited, Trowbridge, Wiltshire.

Your Guarantee of Quality...
As publishers, we strive to produce every book to the highest
commercial standards.
This book has been carefully designed to minimise awkward page
turns and to make playing from it a real pleasure.
Particular care has been given to specifying acid-free, neutral-sized
paper made from pulps which have not been elemental chlorine
bleached. This pulp is from farmed sustainable forests and was
produced with special regard for the environment.
Throughout, the printing and binding have been planned to ensure a
sturdy, attractive publication which should give years of enjoyment.
If your copy fails to meet our high standards, please inform us
and we will gladly replace it.

Music Sales' complete catalogue describes thousands of titles
and is available in full colour sections by subject,
direct from Music Sales Limited. Please state your areas of interest
and send a cheque/postal order for £1.50 for postage to:
Music Sales Limited, Newmarket Road,
Bury St. Edmunds, Suffolk IP33 3YB.

www.internetmusicshop.com

All I Have To Do Is Dream

Words & Music by Boudleaux Bryant

Another Suitcase In Another Hall

Music by Andrew Lloyd Webber
Lyrics by Tim Rice

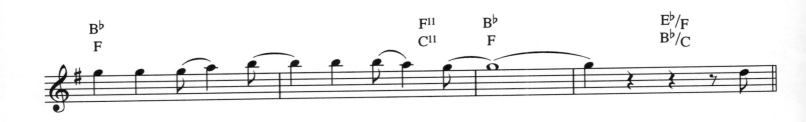

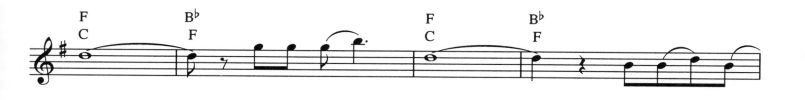

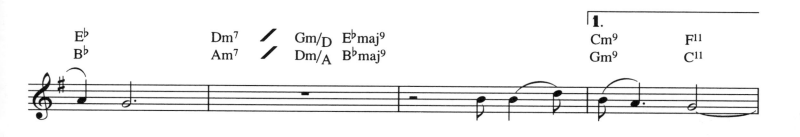

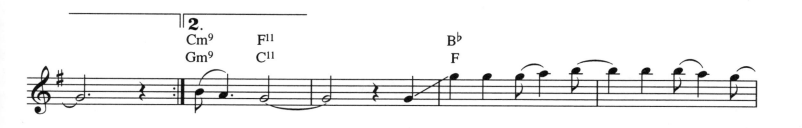

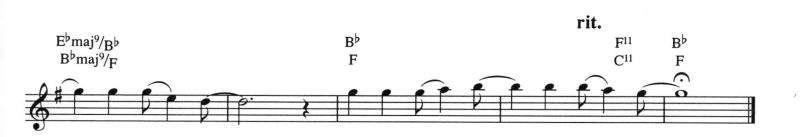

All The Things You Are

Music by Jerome Kern. Words by Oscar Hammerstein II

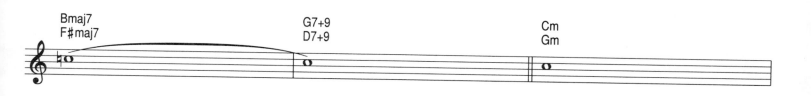

9

Another Day In Paradise

Words & Music by Phil Collins

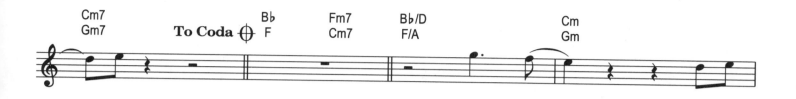

CODA

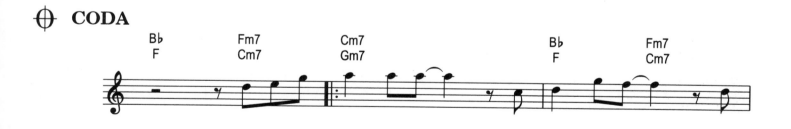

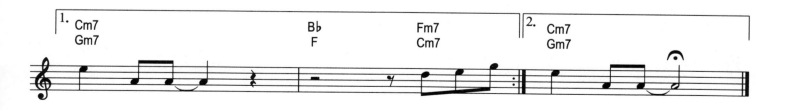

Careless Whisper

Words & Music by George Michael & Andrew Ridgeley

13

Chelsea Bridge

By Billy Strayhorn

Don't Cry For Me Argentina

Music by Andrew Lloyd Webber
Lyrics by Tim Rice

Slow Tango ($\quarternote$ = 76)

Don't Dream Of Anybody But Me (Li'l Darlin')

Words by Bart Howard
Music by Neal Hefti

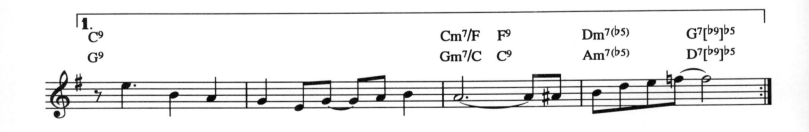

D.C. al Coda

CODA

19

(Everything I Do) I Do It For You

Music by Michael Kamen

21

Georgia On My Mind

Words by Stuart Gorrell
Music by Hoagy Carmichael

Here's That Rainy Day

Words & Music by Johnny Burke & Jimmy Van Heusen

How Insensitive

Music by Antonio Carlos Jobim Original Lyrics by
Vinicius De Moraes English Lyrics by Norman Gimbel

How Deep Is Your Love

Words & Music by Barry Gibb, Robin Gibb & Maurice Gibb

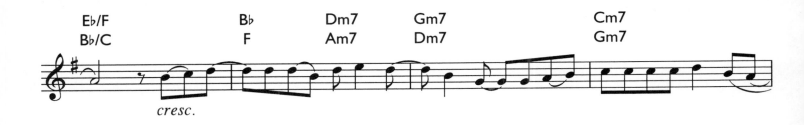

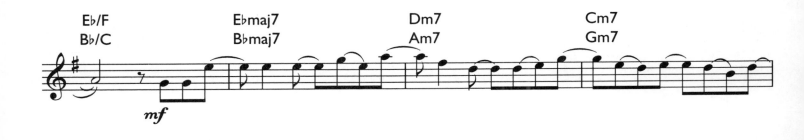

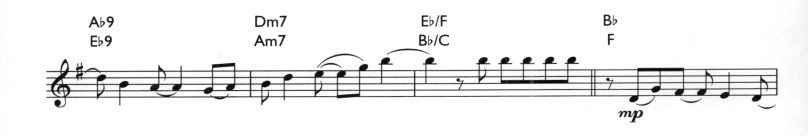

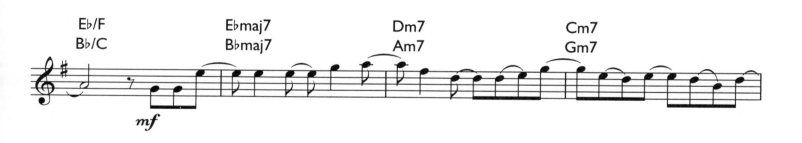

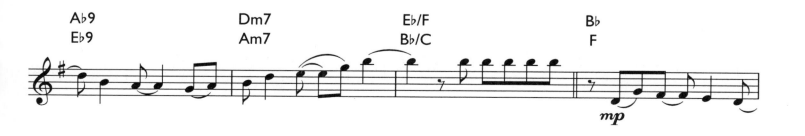

27

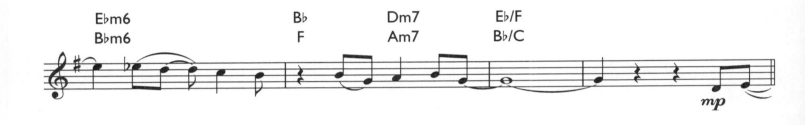

I Just Don't Know What To Do With Myself

Words by Hal David
Music by Burt Bacharach

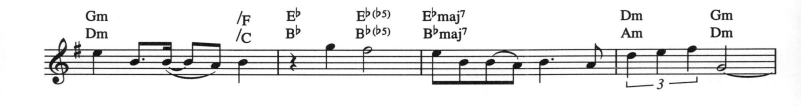

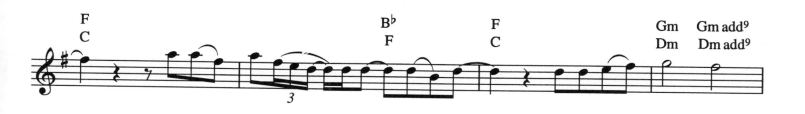

molto dim.

I Still Haven't Found What I'm Looking For

Words & Music by U2

In A Sentimental Mood

Words & Music by Duke Ellington, Irving Mills & Manny Kurtz

33

If I Fell

Words & Music by John Lennon & Paul McCartney

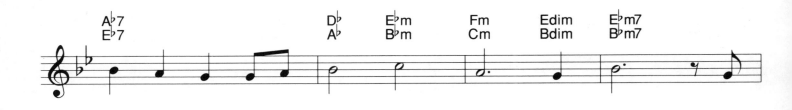

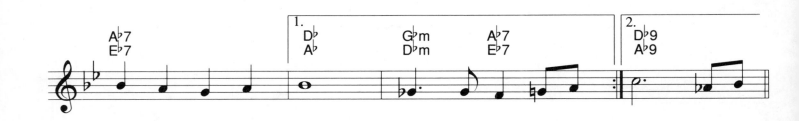

I'll Remember April

Words & Music by Don Raye, Gene de Paul & Patricia Johnson

Killing Me Softly With His Song

Words by Norman Gimbel
Music by Charles Fox

The Lady Sings The Blues

Words by Billie Holiday
Music by Herbie Nichols

Slow blues

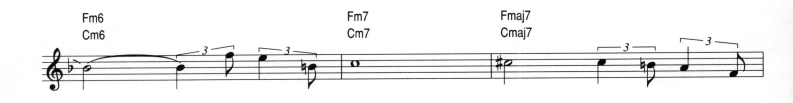

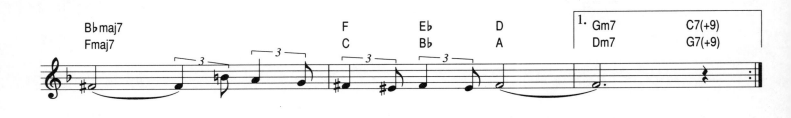

CODA ⊕

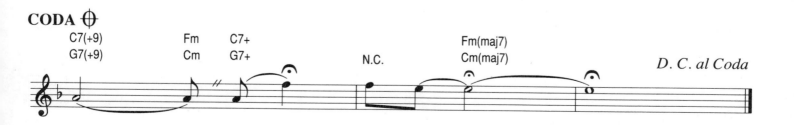

Make It Easy On Yourself

Music by Burt Bacharach
Words by Hal David

43

A Man And A Woman (Un Homme Et Une Femme)

Original Words by Pierre Barouh
English Lyric by Jerry Keller Music by Francis Lai

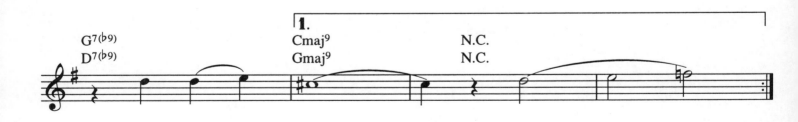

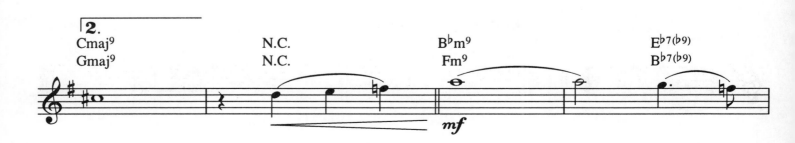

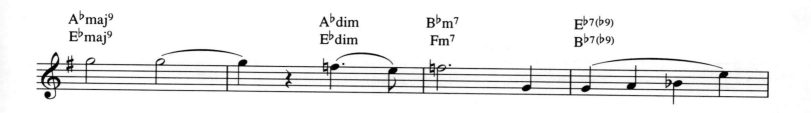

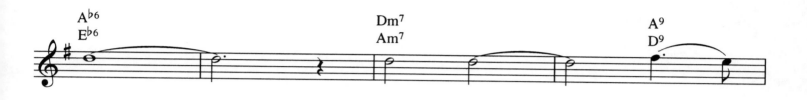

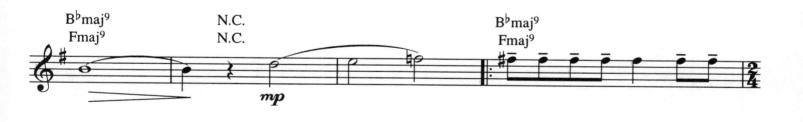

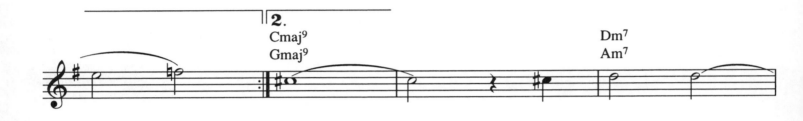

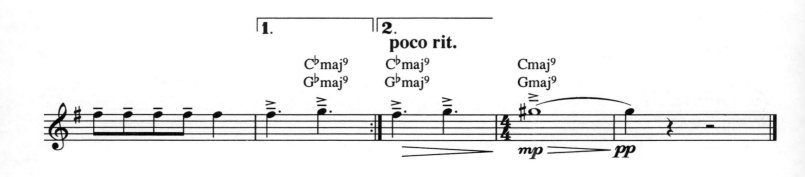

46

Meditation (Meditacao)

Original Words by Newton Mendonca English Lyric by Norman Gimbel
Music by Antonio Carlos Jobim

Michelle

Words & Music by John Lennon & Paul McCartney

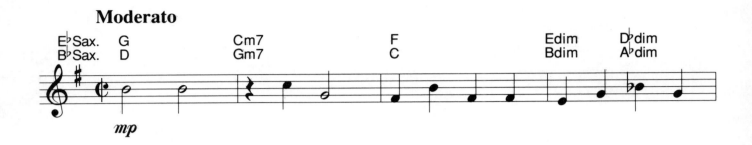

Midnight Sun

Words by Johnny Mercer
Music by Sonny Burke & Lionel Hampton

51

Mona Lisa

Words & Music by Jay Livingston & Ray Evans

Moonglow

Words & Music by Will Hudson, Eddie de Lange & Irving Mills

Moon River

Music by Henry Mancini
Words by Johnny Mercer

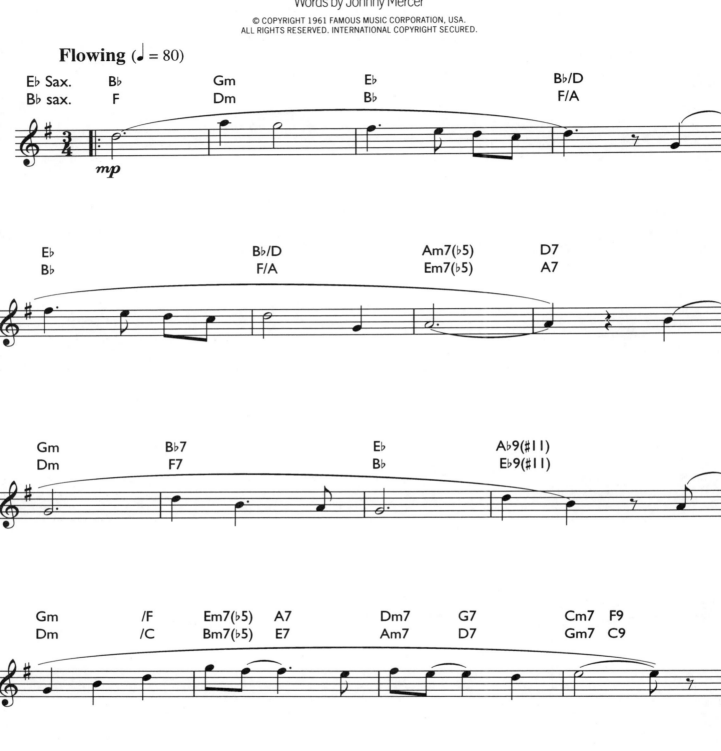

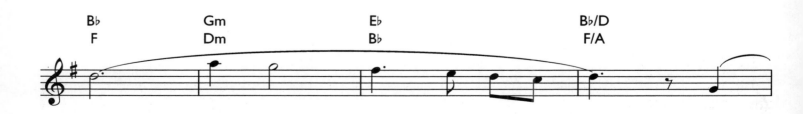

No More "I Love You's"

Words & Music by D. Freeman & J. Hughes

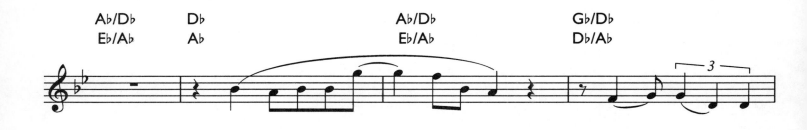

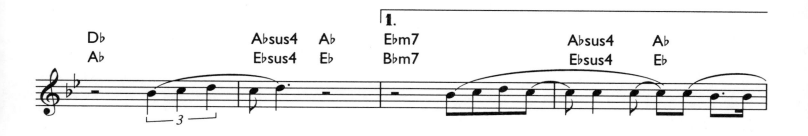

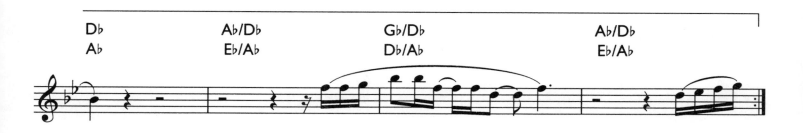

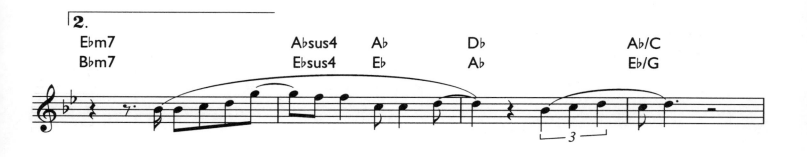

Recado Bossa Nova (The Gift)

Words & Music by Djalma Ferreira & Luiz Antonio

CODA

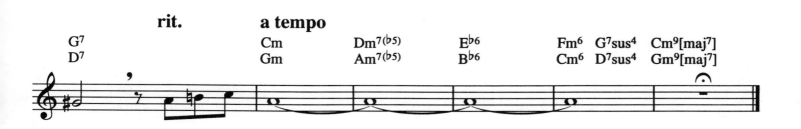

Slightly Out Of Tune (Desafinado)

English Lyric by Jon Hendricks & Jessie Cavanaugh
Music by Antonio Carlos Jobim

Somewhere In Time

By John Barry

Medium slow (♩ = 80)

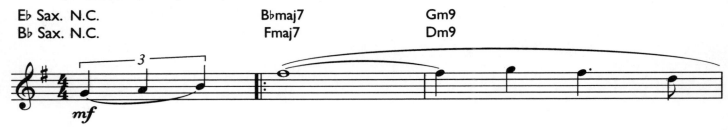

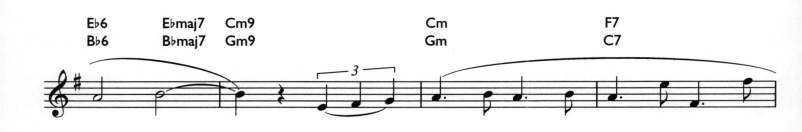

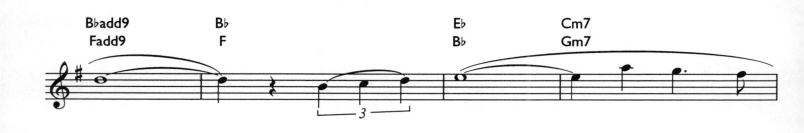

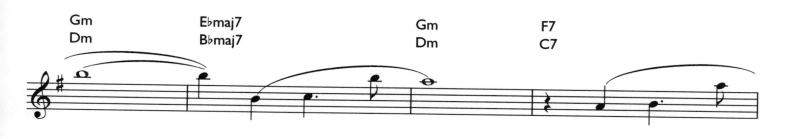

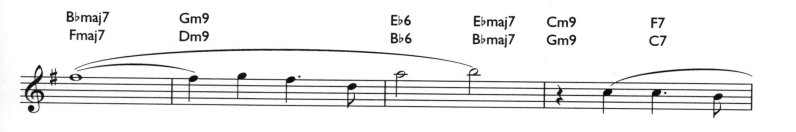

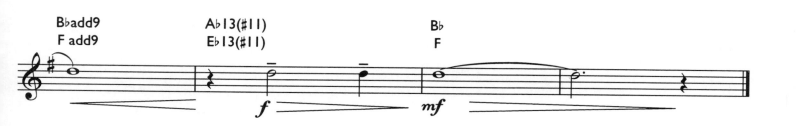

Speak Softly Love

Music by Nino Rota
Words by Larry Kusik

Stars Fell On Alabama

Words by Mitchell Parish
Music by Frank Perkins

Take Five

By Paul Desmond

Moderato

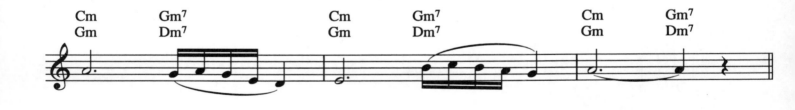

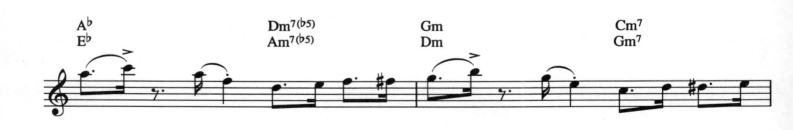

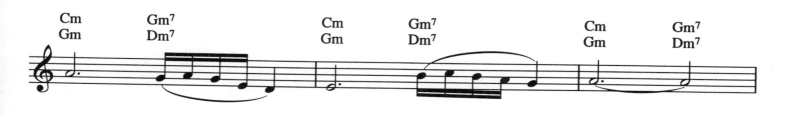

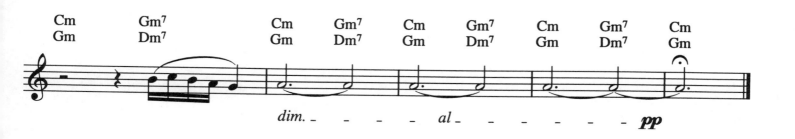

Take My Breath Away

Words by Tom Whitlock
Music by Giorgio Moroder

This Guy's In Love With You

Words by Hal David
Music by Burt Bacharach

A Time For Us (Love Theme from Romeo & Juliet)

Music by Nino Rota
Words by Eddie Snyder & Larry Kusik

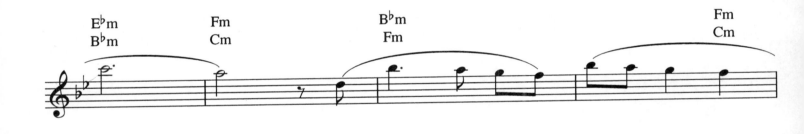

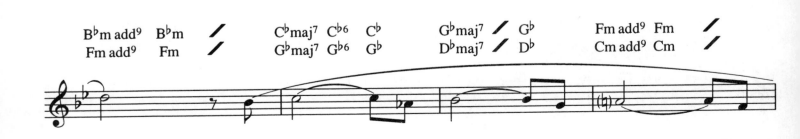

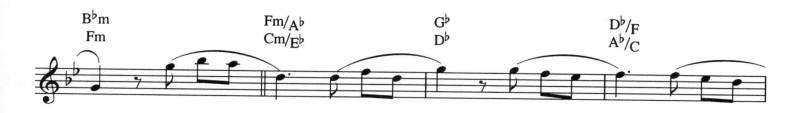

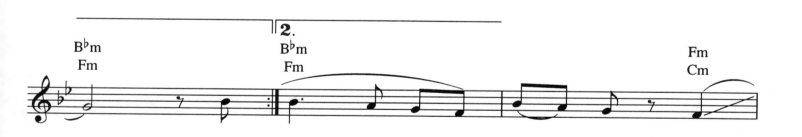

Unchained Melody

Words by Hy Zaret
Music by Alex North

Until It's Time For You To Go

Words & Music by Buffy Sainte-Marie

The Very Thought Of You

Words & Music by Ray Noble

Quiet Nights Of Quiet Stars (Corcovado)

English Words by Gene Lees
Music & Original Words by Antonio Carlos Jobim

Wave

Words & Music by Antonio Carlos Jobim

Walk On By

Music by Burt Bacharach
Words by Hal David

Medium tempo

84

Where Do I Begin (Theme from Love Story)

Music by Francis Lai
Words by Carl Sigman

Medium slow ($\quad$ = 76)

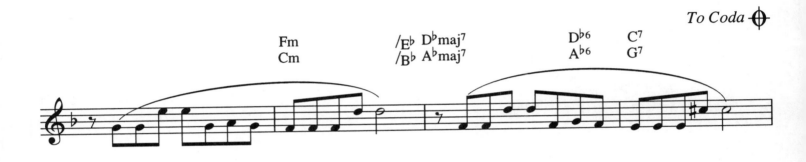

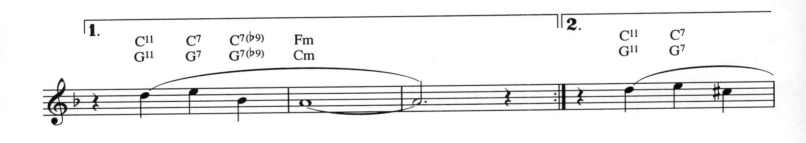

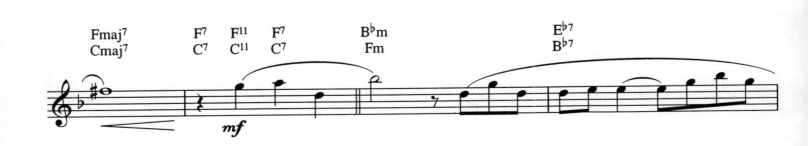

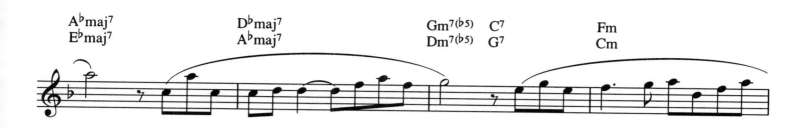

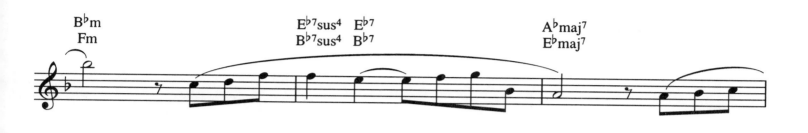

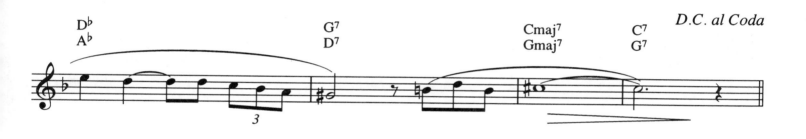

CODA

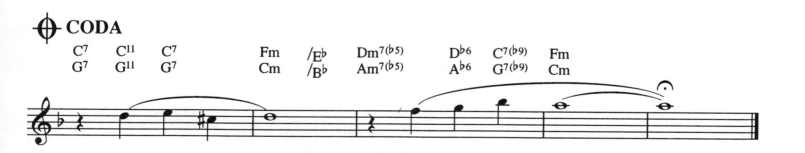

Why

Words & Music by Annie Lennox

89

Words

Words & Music by Barry Gibb, Robin Gibb & Maurice Gibb

poco a poco rit. e dim.

A Whiter Shade Of Pale

Words & Music by Keith Reid & Gary Brooker

Yesterday

Words & Music by John Lennon & Paul McCartney

Moderato

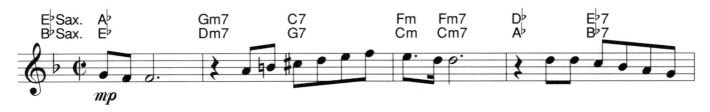

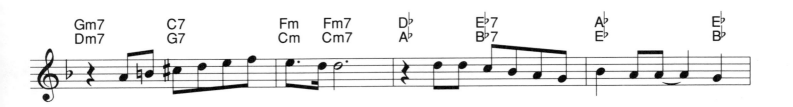

You Are Not Alone

Words & Music by Robert Kelly

Playalong *for* Saxophone

Step into the spotlight with these great CD & Book *titles.*

Playalong with the superb backing tracks on the specially recorded CD... follow the top line arrangements for alto saxophone in the accompanying book.

Titles for alto saxophone in the Guest Spot series include...

Ballads, AM941809

The Beatles, NO90684

Chart Hits, AM955658

Christmas, AM950422

Classic Blues, AM941765

Jazz, AM941721

Film Themes, AM941886

Nineties Hits, AM952875

Showstoppers, AM941842

Swing, AM949399

TV Themes, AM941920

No.1 Hits, AM955625

The CD...

Hear full performance versions of ten songs on Tracks 1-10
The Saxophone part is then omitted from Tracks 11-20 so you can play along with the recorded accompaniments

The Music Book...

Top line arrangements for all ten songs, *plus* Saxophone fingering guide